A HANDWASHING S

TOLD WITH TINY HANDS

A DOING-IS-LEARNING BOOK

By Patricia Prisk • Art by Jason D. McIntosh

WITH SPECIAL THANKS:

For my parents: For teaching me my first "hand story" while sitting in a church pew
For my family: For editing and upgrading my computer skills
For the Many Teachers in my life

ISBN: 978-0-578-87807-2 (print), 978-0-578-87808-9 (ebook) | First Printing 2021

There came a time when everybody in the land decided they needed to keep their hands and their homes

REALLY CLEAN.

Let's make a house.

Can you open the doors of your house? (thumbs)

We cleaned the INSIDE of our home.

First, wash the inside of your hands!

We cleaned the **OUTSIDE** of our home.

Now, wash the outside of your hands!

We cleaned both DOORS.

Next, scrub your thumbs!

Next, we all shampooed our HAIR.

Now, scrub your fingertips!

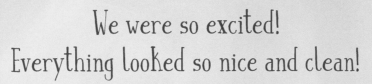

We were so excited!
Everything looked so nice and clean!

LET'S CELEBRATE!

Now, where should the party take place?

Rinse, dry, all done!

OUTSIDE?

Shake those hands!

THE END.

Clap those hands!

HANDWASHING RECAP

Make a hand house.

Scrub the inside.

Wash the outside.

Scrub your thumbs.

Scrub your fingers.

Clean your fingertips.

Rinse, Dry, ALL DONE!

Celebrate outside!

Celebrate inside!

Or choose a new place to celebrate!

Note to Parent/Teacher...

These suggestions are offered to make thorough hand washing EASY for young children to learn. Parents lead very busy lives, and we all appreciate a simpler, hassle-free way to teach and establish good hygiene habits.

1. While reading the story to your child, the reader demonstrates the hand motions with each corresponding page. The hand motions tell the story in a nonverbal way. These hand motions are found on the bottom of each page, using simple drawings to make it easier for you to understand how to do them.

2. Watch for signs from your child that they want to make the hand motions, too. For example, you might notice your child watching you closely as you do the motions, trying to verbalize, or mimic you. Help as needed; or pick the easier hand motions first, such as clapping, washing the inside of the house, or washing the outside of the house. The adult can use hand over hand assistance if the child is really trying to mimic the hand motion but not quite doing the hand movement correctly.

3. Discuss with the child what each hand motion represents. For example, have the child open and close the door to the house (thumbs). Acknowledge, encourage, and praise your child's efforts and accomplishments.

4. Practice and repeat the more complicated hand movements together until they are mastered. Remember to keep the focus on the story and colorful pictures, as they will both entertain and reinforce the sequence of hand washing to the child. Only practice as much as the child wants to. Stop when they are tired, or their attention span is over. Each time you read the story, the child is learning, and hand washing movements are being reinforced.

5. Once a hand motion is mastered, you can then focus on doing the movement 10 times. Count to ten out loud together, while doing the hand movement, eventually doing all the movements ten times each. This will accomplish the goal of washing your hands for 20 seconds or more. (For older children who can do the hand movements at lightened speed, do 12 times each, to meet the 20 second requirement.)

6. Now you are ready to apply soap and water while reciting the story in front of the sink. With a soapy lather, your hands will slip, slide, and glide through the movements. This is a wonderful sensory experience, and it feels great! Actual hand washing is complete after you have "shampooed", rinsed well with water, and then dried your hands with a towel.

7. Added Fun! The story continues as the child is given a choice as to where to have the final celebration. The hand movements continue to tell the story, giving the child a chance to make their own decision as to where the party should be. This adds additional fantasy and fun to the hand washing experience. Best of all, they will have squeaky clean hands!

Classroom Teachers: A "Lunch Time Hand Washing Protocol" for your entire class, which minimizes a backlog at the sink, and video instructions of the hand motions can be obtained by contacting Pat at: ptprisk2021@gmail.com.

SQUEAKY CLEAN

Squeaky Clean Hands Certificate

This certificate is awarded to _____

On this date _____

Congratulations for demonstrating the ability to do the following:

- ☐ **Doing each hand motion while following along in the book!**
- ☐ **Telling the story and doing each hand motion from memory!**
- ☐ **Doing the hand motions 10 times each to have squeaky clean hands!**

⭐ OFFICIAL MEMBER OF THE SQUEAKY CLEAN HANDS CLUB ⭐

I really like my hands to be squeaky clean!

Sign Your Name _____ **Date** _____

A Handwashing Story
Told with Tiny Hands
By Patricia Prisk

This membership entitles the above Club Member to all the health benefits resulting from having squeaky clean hands!

To keep track of your student's accomplishments, cut out this certificate and check off the student's progress. Take photos of your student holding this certificate and post them on social media for family and friends to see and celebrate!

CPSIA information can be obtained
at www.ICGtesting.com
Printed in the USA
LVHW070559160222
711262LV00002B/49